Where Do You Live?

Write about the place that you live using the adjectives (describing words) below to help you.

big, small, warm, cosy, friendly, old, new, busy, modern, colourful, tidy.

Describe your house and draw a picture:

....

....

....

....

....

....

Describe your bedroom and draw a picture:

....

....

....

....

....

....

What's the Order?

Tom's books have fallen on the floor. Put them back in alphabetical order by numbering them from 1-7. The first one has been done for you.

Put these party invitations in alphabetical order by numbering them from 1-6. The first one has been done for you.

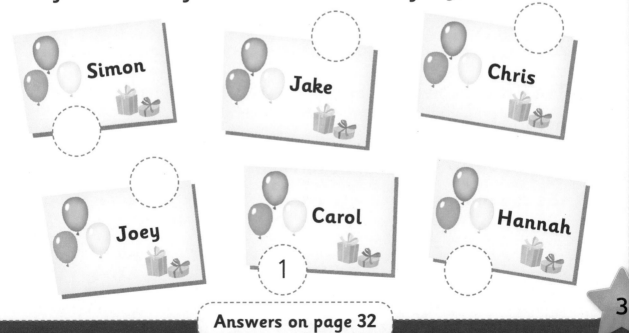

Answers on page 32

Super Spellings

Choose the correct letters from the box below to complete each of these sentences. Each letter combination is used more than once. The first one is done for you.

ay	ou	ie

1. What would you like to pl<u>ay</u>?

2. My h......se is the one on the corner.

3. I need to t...... a knot in the wool.

4. The tr...... was heavy with cups and mugs on it.

5. Do you know anything ab......t bees?

6. That chicken p...... was delicious.

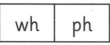

wh	ph

1. Last night we saw a dol<u>ph</u>in swimming in the bay.

2. It was late ......en I got back and Mum asked ......ere I had been.

3. He grabbed the ......eel of the car.

4. An ele......ant never forgets ......ich way to go.

5. The little girl was an or...... an who lived with her uncle and aunt.

6. I don't know ......ich hat to wear, the red one or the ......ite one.

Pancake Perfection

Look at the pictures showing how to make pancakes.
Write an instruction to go with each picture. Can you write
a list of ingredients on the shopping list at the bottom?

1
> Weigh the flour.
> Put it into a mixing bowl.

2

3

Ingredients

1.

2.

3.

4.

4

PARENT TIP: When we write instructions we often start each
sentence with a verb or doing word, such as 'weigh' or 'put'.
This is called 'the imperative form'.

5

Fact or Fiction?

Fiction books are stories or make-believe. Non-fiction means facts or information. Draw lines to show whether you think each book is fiction or non-fiction.

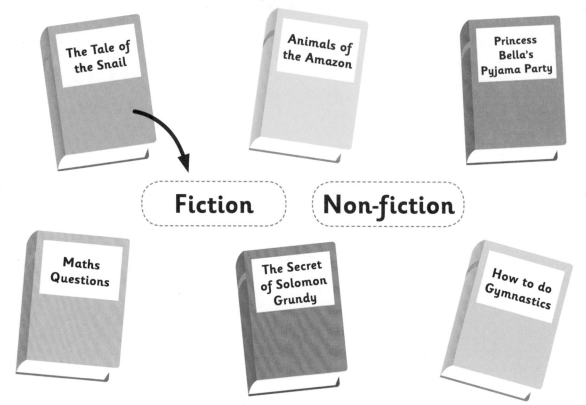

Read these sentences. Write F in the box if it comes from a fiction book. Write N if it comes from a non-fiction book.

1. Coal, oil and gas are all found under the ground.   N

2. When George and his pet dragon woke up, they found the whole kingdom of Merridale had turned pink.

3. Then the magic began. The three girls were taken up into the air in a big swirl of gold dust.

4. The Amazon is home to many kinds of mammals, as well as fish and birds.

5. Sunil opened the door. Outside was a smiling man in a battered, old hat.

6. Some houses are built from bricks and stone, others from wood.

6

Answers on page 32

Rhymes and Tongue-twisters

A tongue-twister is a type of rhyme or poem where lots of the words start with the same sound or letter. Try saying this well known tongue-twister as fast as you can!

Peter Piper picked a peck of pickled pepper.
A peck of pickled pepper Peter Piper picked.
If Peter Piper picked a peck of pickled pepper,
Where's the pickled pepper Peter Piper picked?

Use these boxes of words that start with the same letter to write your own tongue-twister on a separate piece of paper.

> **'p' words:**
> pink, pat, pig, play, pin, point, pass, past,
> pong, paint, pet, peas, penny.

> **'g' words:**
> goat, gate, get, game, great, garden, gang, give, goose.

Silly rhymes use a lot of rhyming words together. Say this rhyme and then try to write your own silly rhyme on a separate piece of paper, using the words in the boxes.

A noisy noise
annoys an oyster most.

 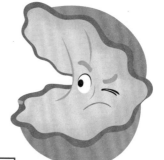

> play, say, day, tray, way, hooray, stray, sway.

> pong, song, long, wrong, ding-dong.

Colour the Sounds

Colour the words in the grid below using this colour key:

'oh' sound		'or' sound		'oo' sound	
e.g. 'wind<u>ow</u>', 't<u>oe</u>'		e.g. 'fl<u>oor</u>', 'cl<u>aw</u>'		e.g. 'ch<u>ew</u>', 'gl<u>ue</u>'	
true	boat	window	hollow	throw	ball
clue	row	arrow	mow	show	claw
two	tissue	toe	hoe	snore	caught
chew	threw	no	snow	four	law
crew	glue	slow	echo	your	sore
too	flew	coat	goes	floor	raw
who	sue	low	float	saw	roar
blue	brew	so	know	taught	short
drew	knew	solo	hello	daughter	talk
shoe	stew	goat	bow	pour	hall

How many words have you coloured...

blue? ◯

yellow? ◯

purple? ◯

What letter shape can you see in the yellow words?

....

Answers on page 32

PARENT TIP: At this stage in their phonics, children are learning that one sound can be spelt in different ways. The three vowel sounds above can be represented by several different letter combinations, or graphemes.

Here 'e' Comes

Complete these words using the letter combinations below.
Find the missing sticker for the completed word in each row.

i_e	e_e	a_e	u_e	o_e

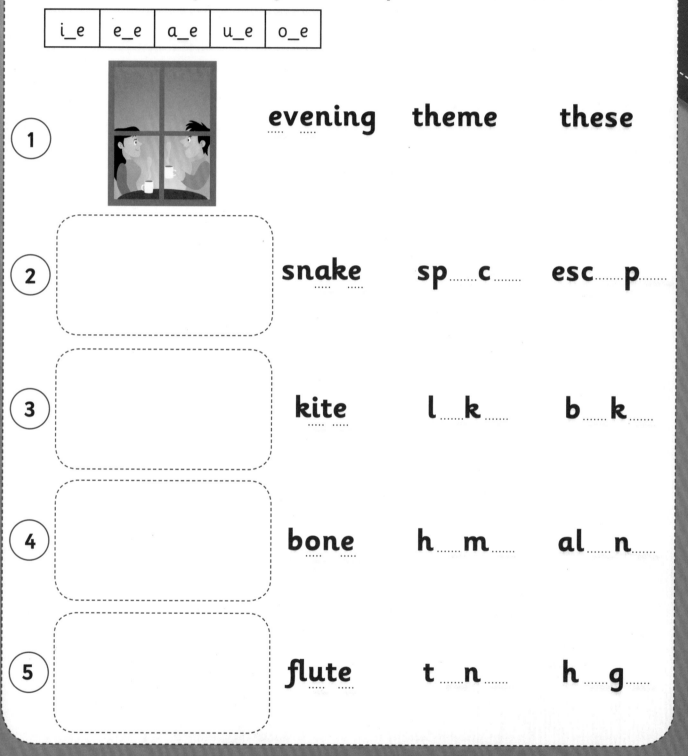

1   evening   theme   these

2   snake   sp___c___   esc___p___

3   kite   l___k___   b___k___

4   bone   h___m___   al___n___

5   flute   t___n___   h___g___

PARENT TIP: Often when we add the letter 'e' to the end of a word,
the 'e' makes the vowel in the middle of the word 'say its name'.
For example, when 'slid' becomes 'slide', the short 'i' sound
says the letter name 'i'.

9

Compound Nouns

Choose the correct word to complete each compound noun jigsaw. The first one is done for you.

place	ground	stand	~~yard~~

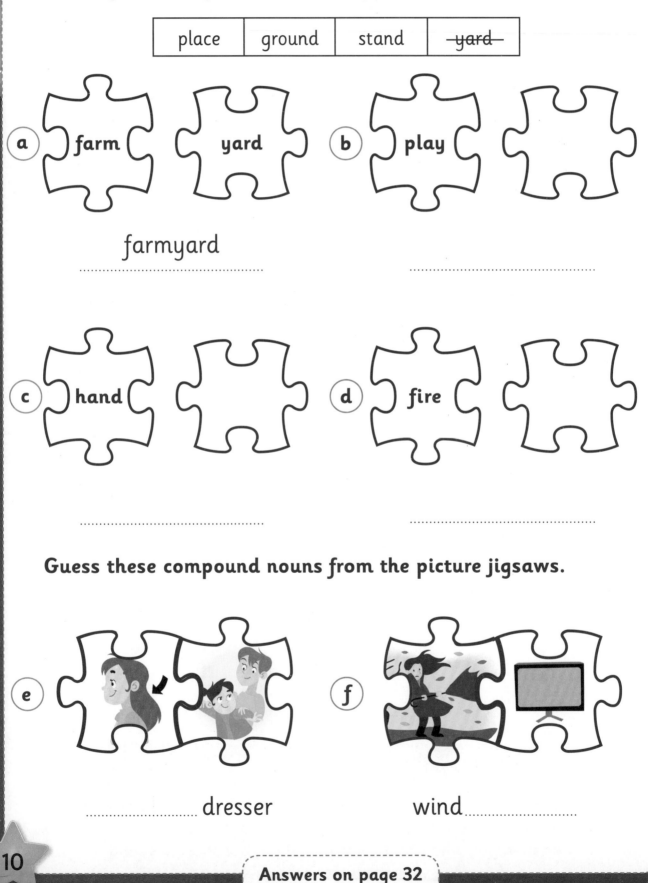

a) farm · yard

farmyard
....

b) play

....

c) hand

....

d) fire

....

Guess these compound nouns from the picture jigsaws.

e) .... dresser

f) wind ....

Answers on page 32

Circus Spellings

Read these high-frequency words, cover each word after you read it, then write it on a separate piece of paper. Check to see if you spelt it right and add some circus stickers.

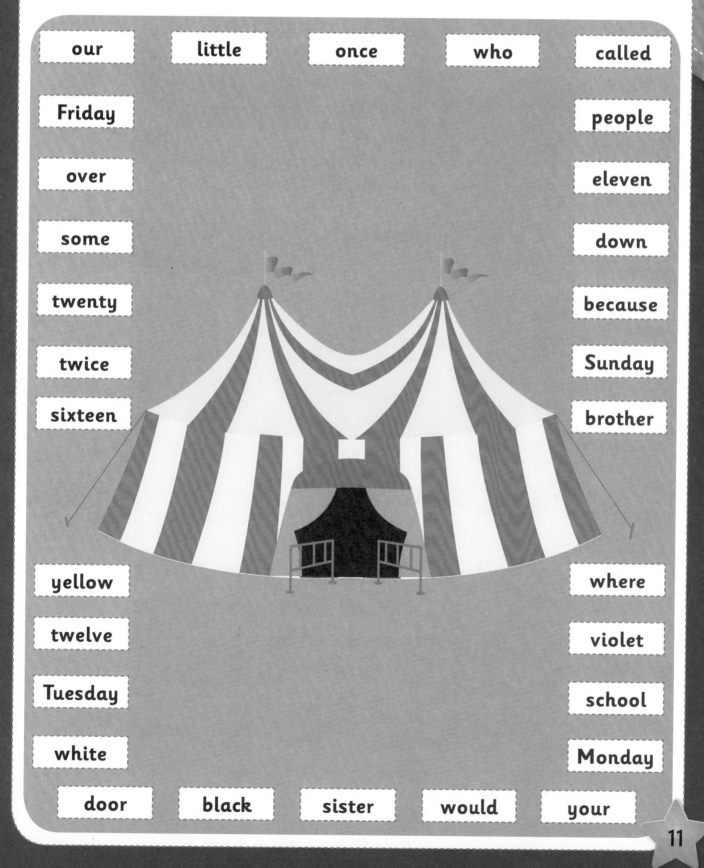

our	little	once	who	called
Friday				people
over				eleven
some				down
twenty				because
twice				Sunday
sixteen				brother
yellow				where
twelve				violet
Tuesday				school
white				Monday
door	black	sister	would	your

Which Way to the Cinema?

Write directions from the house to the cinema using the words in the box to help you. The first one has been done for you.

> past, left, right, straight on, turn, go, around, over, cross, walk, along, corner, road.

Directions:
After leaving the house, turn right. Walk along the street to the corner.

....

....

....

....

Chips on the Pitch?

Find the 'ch' and 'tch' words in the word search.
Write each word you find in the correct list underneath.

chip, chair, rich, march, porch, each, hutch, hitch,
crutch, watch, pitch, catch.

c	h	i	p	o	r	c	h
a	m	z	i	v	i	e	u
t	b	l	t	q	c	s	t
c	c	o	c	m	h	w	c
h	h	j	h	i	t	c	h
m	a	m	a	r	c	h	t
c	i	g	w	l	s	d	e
c	r	u	t	c	h	h	a
b	f	k	r	x	p	h	c
o	l	d	w	a	t	c	h

'tch' words
pitch
....
....
....
....
....
....

'ch' words
chip
....
....
....
....
....
....

Answers on page 32

PARENT TIP: Where the 'ch' sound is heard, it is usually spelt with either a 'ch' or 'tch'. Usually, 'tch' only appears at the end of words, normally after a short vowel, e.g. patch. 'ch' can appear anywhere.

I Spy Spellings

Sophie is having a wonderful dream. Look at all the things she's dreaming about and write them under the correct phoneme below. The first ones have been done for you.

donkey, game, thief, ~~tray~~, sky, monkey, crayons, slide, field, chief, tie, snake, ~~sea~~, prize, pie, ~~rice~~.

'ay' (as in s<u>a</u>me)	'ee' (as in funn<u>y</u>)	'igh' (as in repl<u>y</u>)
tray	sea	rice

Answers on page 32

PARENT TIP: Remember that two words can contain the same phoneme sound without having the same letters, e.g. 'd<u>ry</u>'/'c<u>r</u>i<u>ed</u>'. The phonemes in this activity can be spelt in several different ways.

What Happened Next?

Number the boxes to put the story in the correct order.

a So, the little sparrow went to see Robin. "I'd like a nice, red chest like yours," the sparrow said. "Well," said Robin, "to get a nice red chest like mine you must find and eat the reddest berries."

b Once upon a time, there was a little sparrow who was very unhappy. "I'm bored with being a small, brown bird," he told the other sparrows in the old barn. "I want to be a beautiful bird with colourful feathers." **1**

c The other birds clustered around him as he told his sad tale. "You may not be beautiful like a robin, or a flamingo," said his mum, "but you will always be beautiful to us, just because we love you." The little sparrow smiled. At last, he really did feel beautiful.

d Sparrow wasn't keen on berries, so he went away to ask the flamingos in the zoo. They were huge and pink with long, graceful necks. Sparrow went to the most beautiful of the birds. "I want to be beautiful, like you," he said.

e "That's easy," said the flamingo. "You must eat little pink shrimps all day." That didn't sound easy to Sparrow. He didn't like shrimps at all! Sparrow began to feel sad. "I will never be beautiful like the robin, or the flamingo," he thought. He flew back to the old barn, where his friends and family were perched.

Answers on page 32

Sweet Treats

Say the words below out loud. Join each word with a long 'ee' sound to the tray of sweet treats. There are 12 words without long 'ee' sound.

sunny

shield

blew

may

plume

bread

honey

priest

heap

fried

bead

amaze

brief

sugar

note

knee

head

ditch

penny

mix

only

sweet

fetch

crease

treat

Answers on page 32

Who Said That?

Add speech marks in the correct places below to show the direct speech in each example. Join each word box to the correct person. The first one has been done for you.

a

1 "I started work early today as I want to finish Mr Jenkins' new shed," says Mr Trowell the builder. "Then I am off to do a job at the railway station."

b

2 Today I am going to make some beautiful sponge cakes for my restaurant, says head chef Mr Baker. I hope the customers like them.

3 I am very busy today. I have to look at George's sore throat, and then check Mrs Hagan's bad knee, said Dr Smith. Then I might have a break and a cup of tea.

c

d

4 I take Mr Tickles for a walk in the park every day, said Mrs Pinkson. When we get home I give him a biscuit.

Answers on page 32

Noun, Verb, Adjective

Look at all the words bubbling in the soup. Decide whether each word is a verb (action word), a noun (thing or object) or an adjective (describing word). Write it in the correct list.

ball
~~make~~

mummy
beautiful
~~badge~~

horse
machine
want

bright
catch

star
~~ugly~~

stare
drive

climb
silly

tall
soft

Verbs

make

....

....

....

....

....

Nouns

badge

....

....

....

....

....

Adjectives

ugly

....

....

....

....

....

What a Question!

Decide whether each of these sentences needs a full stop or a question mark at the end. The first one has been done for you.

1. Do you know which road I should take to get to the college?

2. I need to know the answer to this question immediately_

3. This is the best time of year to plant tomatoes_

4. How do you know that this is the best time_
   Is it because it is sunny_

5. What do you know about cooking_
   This cake has come out all wrong_

6. When the long hand reaches twelve, I will start the clock_

Choose a question word from the box to start each sentence. The first one has been done for you.

When	What	How	Where	Which	~~Do~~

1. Do you know the way to the hospital?

2. .... is the cheese that I was saving for my sandwich?

3. .... do I put this tent up? It has no pegs.

4. .... is your dog called? Mine is called Fido.

5. .... is it time to open the presents?

6. .... is the right hat?

A Sound Landing

Look at the phonemes in the box and read the words in the grid. Decide which phoneme can be found in each word and colour the words to match the phonemes.
Which phoneme pathway leads to Earth?

'ur' sound as in g<u>ir</u>l			'eer' sound as in sp<u>ear</u>		
curtain	girl	gear	steer	first	ear
hear	worse	earth	worth	hurl	fur
sheer	deer	whirl	curl	spear	tear
career	cheer	leer	her	certain	shirt
beer	fear	near	here	hurt	burst
skirt	dear	bird	worm	birth	insert
year	third	herb	perky	pearl	person

Start

Finish

This kangaroo can only land on words that have the phoneme 'air', as in 'bear'. Draw a circle around each word with an 'air' sound.

Start

wear	wing	nowhere	about
bear	air	where	hare
face	know	twig	care
rare	whale	please	stare

Finish

Can the kangaroo jump across the grid to reach the stream? ☐

Answers on page 32

Then There Were More

When we want to say that there is more than one of something, we use the 'plural'. For example, the plural of sweet is 'sweets'. Read these sentences and decide which words need to be made plural by adding 's' or 'es'.

1. When I woke up the room was filled with present**s** and cards sending me best wish**es**.

2. I love riding horse..... and this one is my favourite. I visit him in the stable..... with some oat..... every day.

3. Tom was bragging that he had two watch..... . One watch had hand..... on it and the other was digital.

4. I tried to put the light on but there were so many switch..... that I couldn't find the right one. It was so dark I couldn't see my own finger.....!

5. There are probably many planet....., moon....., star..... and other thing..... in space that we have not yet seen.

When a word ends in 'y', we don't add just 's' or 'es'. Cross out the 'y' and replace it with 'ies' to make the words in these sentences plural.

1. I love bab**ies**, but their crying hurts my ears.

2. Please don't drop the jelly....... . They have only just set.

3. I need to take my welly....... off and put my slippers on.

4. I thought I could hear some cry....... for help, but it was only a seagull.

5. Those lady....... over there have the nicest cakes.

22

Phoneme Detectives

Underline and put a spyglass sticker above each word containing the phoneme 'oo', as in cl<u>ue</u>, or 'sh' as in <u>s</u>ugar.

It was the 25th of <u>June</u>. I had a few moments to kill so I

<u>shoved</u> my way through to the front of the queue at the cafe.

Positioned between a few ladies reading crossword clues,

I spotted a man with a blue book on the other side of

the room. He blew on his coffee. He looked at me.

He chewed on his spoon.

Who was he? Before I could be sure, he stood up suddenly,

spilling sugar. The chef shouted out, "Hey, watch what you

are doing!" Something about the man made me shudder.

With a huge gulp of coffee, I set off to pursue him.

He was hard to follow in the gloom and as it

grew darker, I lost him, but I did find one clue.

It was a tissue and on it was written, 'Sue'.

Find the Hidden Treasure

Read the clues and follow the directions to find the hidden treasure. Check your answer at the back of the book and put a treasure chest sticker in the right place on the grid.

(1) Steer your ship to the beach at E10.

(2) Walk up four spaces.

(3) Oh no, crocodile! Go three spaces to the left.

(4) Try to cross the volcano by going down one space and three spaces to the left.

(5) Go down two spaces to avoid the lava.

(6) Oh no, quicksand! Go down two spaces and two spaces to the left and take shelter in the cave.

(7) It's a dragon's cave! Run out of the cave and go two spaces up to find the treasure.

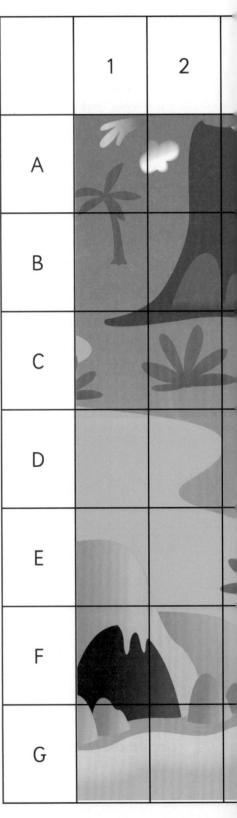

	1	2
A		
B		
C		
D		
E		
F		
G		

Can you think of a pirate name for this island? Write it in the box below the directions.

4	5	6	7	8	9	10	11	12

Answers on page 32

Hide Your Own Treasure

Decide where to hide your own treasure on this grid and draw a map. Write your own instructions to someone else to help them find it. Use imperatives, e.g. 'Walk three spaces to the left'.

	1	2	3	4	5	6	7
A							
B							
C							
D							
E							
F							
G							

To find the treasure...

....

....

....

....

....

....

....

Haunted House

Read this spooky poem out loud:

Haunted house on the hill,
Windows dark and curtains still,
Rooms asleep in quiet chill.

Through the doorway, in you sneak,
Down the hall, the floorboards creak.

Up the stairs, the portraits shift,
An old clock chimes, the curtains drift.

Look around, what's hiding here?
Is it just the dark you fear?

Listen hard, a step behind...
Some things are best not to find.

Haunted house on the hill,
All awake and waiting still.

Can you write a short poem about a creepy house like this one?
Use the picture and the words in the box to help you.

creak	sneak	chill	shrill	old	cold
gloom	room	stairs	hairs	dark	spark

....

....

....

....

....

....

....

Monster Crossword

Complete the crossword all about this monster.

Across

1. This monster scratches his head with his <u>claws</u>.
5. The monster's eyes are .... shaped.
6. The monster has .... arms, like a spider.
7. He has a long nose, or ....
9. This monster's ears are round,
   or ....

Down

2. This monster's head is <u>lumpy</u>.
3. The monster has long ....
   on his chin.
4. His fur is the colour ....
8. The monster is the opposite of beautiful!

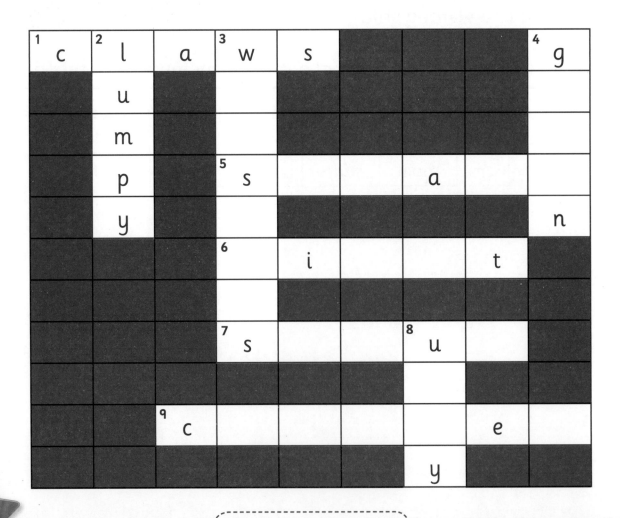

Answers on page 32

Alien Anagrams

Unscramble these alien names to make everyday words. Draw lines to join each anagram to the correct words and find the missing stickers.

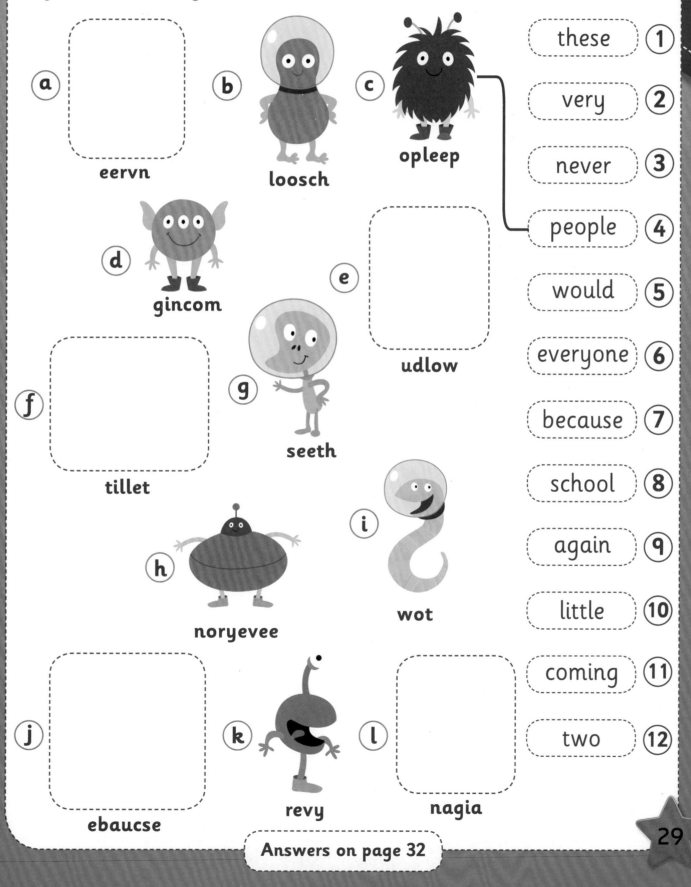

a **eervn**

b **loosch**

c **opleep**

d **gincom**

e **udlow**

f **tillet**

g **seeth**

h **noryevee**

i **wot**

j **ebaucse**

k **revy**

l **nagia**

1 these
2 very
3 never
4 people
5 would
6 everyone
7 because
8 school
9 again
10 little
11 coming
12 two

Answers on page 32

29

My Diary

Write a diary of your typical week.
What kind of things do you get up to?
Put a star sticker by your favourite day.

Monday

....

....

....

....

....

Tuesday

....

....

....

....

Wednesday

....

....

....

Thursday

....

....

....

....

Friday

....

....

....

....

....

Saturday

....

....

....

....

Sunday

....

....

....

....

Answers

Page 3: What's the Order?

1 – Dinosaurs, 2 – Dogs,
3 – Lizards and Reptiles,
4 – Moths and Butterflies,
5 – Sea Creatures,
6 – Space Travel, 7 – Stick Insects

1 – Carol, 2 – Chris, 3 – Jake,
4 – Joey, 5 – Hannah, 6 – Simon

Page 6: Fact or Fiction?

1 – N, 2 – F, 3 – F, 4 – N, 5 – F,
6 – N

Page 8 – Colour the Sounds

There are 18 blue images.
There are 24 yellow images.
There are 18 purple images.
The yellow words make the letter shape 'T'.

Page 10: Compound Nouns

a – farmyard, b – playground,
c – handstand, d – fireplace,
e – hairdresser, f – windscreen

Page 13: Chips on the Pitch?

'ch' = purple, 'tch' = orange

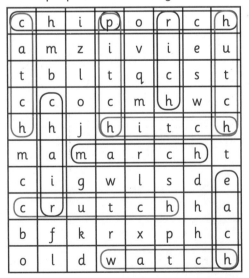

Page 16: What Happened Next?

a – 2, b – 1, c – 5, d – 3, e – 4

Page 14: I Spy Spellings

'ay' words – tray, crayons, game, snake.
'ee' words – sea, field, chief, thief, monkey, donkey
'igh' words – pie, tie, rice, slide, prize, sky

Page 17: Sweet Treats

Words without an 'ee' sound: blew, bread, may, plume, fried, amaze, sugar, head, ditch, mix, fetch.

Page 18: Who Said That?

a – 3, b – 4, c – 1, d – 2

Page 21 – A Sound Landing

The 'ur' (yellow) pathway leads to Earth.
Yes, the kangaroo can reach the stream.

Page 24 – Find the Treasure

The treasure is at D2.

Page 28 – Monster Crossword

1c	2l		3w	s			4g
	u		h				r
	m		i				e
	p		5s	q	u	a	r	e
	y		k				n
			6e	i	g	h	t
			r				
			7s	n	o	8u	t
						g	
	9c	i	r	c	l	e	s
						y	

Page 29 – Alien Anagrams

a – 3, b – 8, c – 4, d – 11, e – 5, f – 10,
g – 1, h – 6, i – 12, j – 7, k – 2, l – 9